TRUMPLETHINSKIN
IN THE LAND OF UCK

Tiny Hands Press
an imprint of DRPZ Publishing
drpz.net

*except for Trumplethinskin

TRUMPLETHINSKIN IN THE LAND OF UCK

Martin Treanor

DEDICATION

Martin Treanor—for it is again he—would like to thank the boundless ridiculousness of life, the Universe, and everything. Especially humans, who have an almost inexhaustible capacity for doing the very thing that is detrimental to them.

So, thank you all.

Without that ludicrousness, this book would never have happened.

Many leagues from Trumplethinskin's realm of *Not Far Far Away Enough*, across a wide, wide sea, there lay the mysterious Land of UcK. It was a strange place, where people spoke as if their mouths were full of marbles and everyone in the land lived in grand palaces, except for paupers—which was what they called people without golden toilets there—who liked their queen but not the court jester, Bojo the Bozo.

According to *Fibber Fox's Tall Tall Tales*, and just like Trumplethinskin himself, Bojo was very, very, very intelligent, and had many, many beautiful, incredible, and beautiful ideas. He was also a stable genius, who ran around saying he would "*get it done*"—whatever *it* was—and Hennity Bennity promised Trumplethinskin he would make a very good friend and give loads of lovely presents: free trade stuff and something called a *health service*, although no one in Trumplethinskin's realm knew what a health service was.

Apparently, the Land of UcK was going through something called a *Brexit*, which sounded like breakfast, and breakfast was something Trumplethinskin liked very much.

Anyway, it seemed that Brexit meant the Land of UcK had fallen out with their best friends next door and were running around like headless chickens looking for new ones—or one—in fact; they would be friends with anybody.

So, upon hearing the news, Trumplethinskin gathered up his roly-poly belly, ran a brush through his wispy, fly-away hair, made his jowly face more orange than it had ever been, and headed off with his latest princess, Malificenia, who Trumplethinskin had met when he was staying with—and asking favors from—his bestest-in-all-the-world friend, the evil pixie, Pootie Poot.

And off he went, across the wide, wide sea, landed in the Land of UcK and, upon arriving, was greeted by so many people he couldn't count them. Which wasn't surprising because, just like words, Trumplethinskin *"didn't count good either."*

The people had placards and were shouting at him—words of welcome, no doubt—saying things like: *Bugger Off, Take Bojo with You*, and *Keep Your Tiny Baby Hands Off Our NHS*—whatever an NHS was—maybe it was a type of beautiful chocolate cake. Trumplethinskin really liked beautiful chocolate cake.

Anyway, after that rousing, fond welcome, he demanded to visit the Queen of the Land of UcK at her grand palace where he partook of something called *afternoon tea*.

The Queen was there.

Her son, his old friend, Andy Handsy, was there.

Some other—not important—people were there.

One of the local town criers, the Pied Moron, who really wanted to meet Trumplethinskin but whom nobody liked, however, wasn't there and spent his time begging at the big palace gates to be let in. He was crying like a softy snowflake—nearly as much as Trumplethinskin did when people said truthful but very nasty things about him.

And, outside the window, the clamor of the crowd down below echoed around the throne room and reminded him of the many people who frequently turned up outside his second home at the Bigly Big White House (white being Trumplethinskin's favorite color), shouting at the top of their voices that he should be given a load of peaches. Which was nice. But Trumplethinskin didn't eat fruit. Fruit was for losers. Fruit was *fake news*. He only ate huge slabs of beautiful chocolate cake. Of which there was none at this *afternoon-tea* thing. The sandwiches were tiny, cut into triangles, with cucumber inside. Cucumber was a vegetable, which was just like loser, *fake news* fruit. There were scones, though, but they were tinier even than the sandwiches.

He was starving. How was he to maintain his roly-poly belly with snacks like these?

Luckily, Bojo the Bozo turned up with a chocolate cake he'd bought from Old Macdonald. And Trumplethinskin was the happiest person alive.

When he had scoffed the lot, Trumple-thinskin plonked his chubby ass down into a chair, smiled at the Queen—who didn't smile back, may I add—and surveyed the palace throne room.

Trumplethinskin didn't have a throne room, or even a throne. Trumplethinskin wanted a throne—a real throne—not just a golden toilet. So much so, he got even crotchetier than usual, whinged, cried, stomped his feet.

"Wah – wah – wah," he bawled and bawled and bawled. "Get me a throne. And get me one now!" he shouted at Pompelo, his elf who did the buying of things.

"They're all taken," Pompelo replied. "And, anyway, only proper kings and queens get to have thrones."

Trumplethinskin stomped his bonespur-less feet.

"I *am* a proper king," he huffed. "Everyone says so. I am the bestest king. And I want my throne, now!" he bawled.

"But there aren't any left."

"Then get me the Queen of UcK's one."

Pompelo did his thinking dance.

"That might work," he said, finally. "In fact, with Bojo having fallen out with his neighbors, and running around trying to make friends with all and sundry, there is a good chance you could buy up every corner of the Land of UcK."

Trumplethinskin smiled, which was rare, seeing how he only ever scowled, huffed, whinged, moaned, and bawled.

"You can lie that Bojo will get access to some of Daddy Trumplethinskin's big bulging bag of magic beans," Pomelo continued. "It'll be easy peasy. He is so desperate for friends he'll give you anything you want. The whole of the Land of UcK will be yours . . . even the throne."

Which was funny, because *Not Far Far Away Enough* once belonged to the Land of UcK, when it was called Great, Magnificent, Brilliant Britland and owned the world, which was what Trumplethinskin wanted to do.

color me in!

Happy, for now at least, Trumplethinskin retired to his bedroom in the grand palace of the Queen of the Land of UcK, ate a giant slab of beautiful chocolate cake, and fell sound asleep.

He dreamed of maybe getting a throne, about huge golf courses, Malificenia (who didn't sleep in the same bed with him anymore—not that she ever did), and how someday he would be king of everywhere.

So far, he owned his own realm. By way of Bojo the Bozo, he would soon own the Land of UcK. And he had already asked Pomelo to look into buying the Isle of Green at the top of the world.

There were, however, three places he knew he could never have: Pootie Poot's Kingdom of Rushes; the Genie Jin's land of china plates; and the dark northern realm that was ruled by the evil sorcerer, Kim. Just like Vet Nam, Kim's realm was a scary place, and Kim was clever—almost as clever as Trumplethinskin and, just like Trumplethinskin, he had rockets, even though he said he didn't and Trumple-thinskin believed every word he said.

But that, again, is another story altogether.

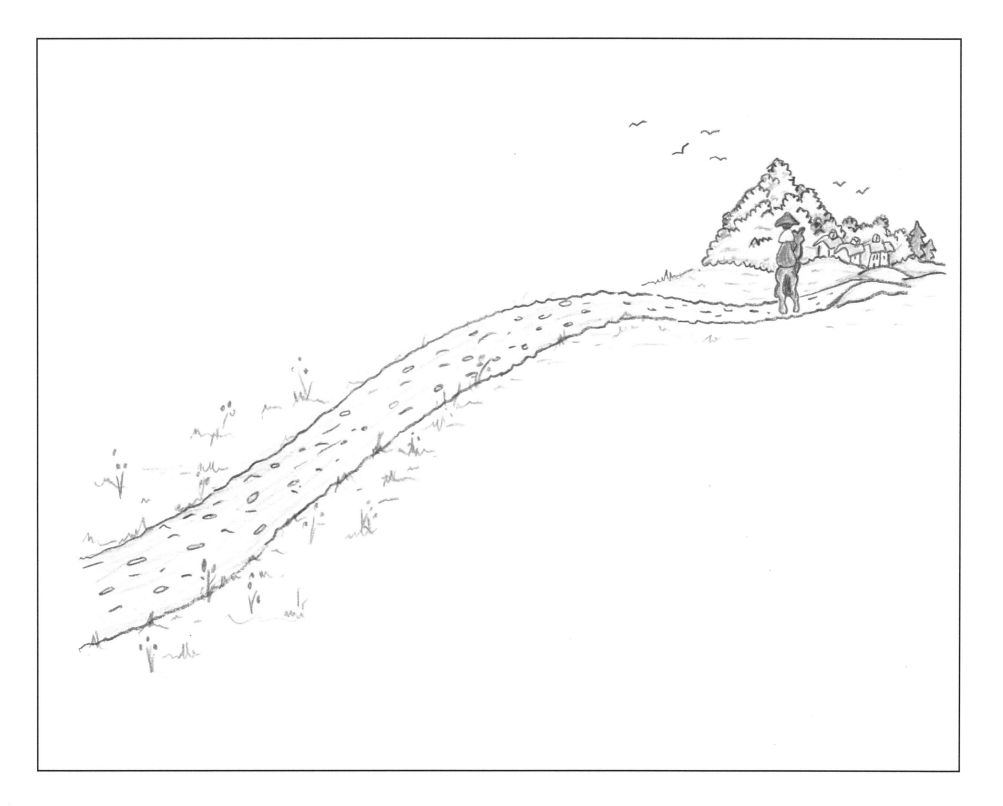

ABOUT THE AUTHOR

Martin Treanor is an author and illustrator—which didn't really need saying, because he writes and illustrates all the Trumplethinskin books. He likes coffee, cake, and cake—doesn't live anywhere snazzy but he did write two other cool books: *The Silver Mist* and *Dark Creed*. He also wrote a load of short stories too . . . oh, and illustrated some other stuff.
He likes cake.

More at: *www.MartinTreanor.com*
Martin Treanor is represented by
DRPZ™ [www.drpz.net]

Look for our thin-skinned "hero" in
Trumplethinskin and the Wizard Bonespurs and
Trumplethinskin and the Gigantic Peach!

For more information about this Very Stable Genius, please visit:

TheTalesOfTrumplethinskin.com
MartinTreanor.com
ANiceCuppaTea.com

@TrumpleTales

TINY HANDS

PRESS

RATCATCHERS

Ye Olde Dating Service for Fickle Folk

NAME: Trumplethinskin (second attempt)
OCCUPATION: Throne aficionado and super duper accumulator of magic beans
LIKES: Magic beans, thrones, and golden toilets
DISLIKES: Nasty reporters who ask questions
BEST QUALITY: Knows everything better than all the experts
WORST QUALITY: None—I am bestest best at everything
FAVORITE FOOD: Still beautiful chocolate cake
FAVORITE THING: Me

PROFILE:

This is my second go at this—my previous attempt not receiving a single response. But that's fake news for you. I still live in *Not Far Far Away Enough* and will, one day, definitely be king of the world. My roly-poly belly has gotten bigger since my last entry—and, therefore, lovelier, and my beautiful orange face shines like the sun in the sky. Get with me and I'll show you the best two seconds of your life—down on my last estimate, I know, but that's only because of the stress of having to ignore questions about things I actually did and said. Again, no elves, hobgoblins, or pixies—as I only make dodgy deals with those. Oh, and definitely no nasty reporters . . . they're the worst.

CPSIA information can be obtained
at www.ICGtesting.com
Printed in the USA
BVHW061804050822
643900BV00011B/827